# A SUFFOL[ ] BOOK

*What and where is this building?*

COVER QUESTIONS.
*Front: Where is this House in the Clouds?*
*Back:: In which town does the gatehouse to*
*a palace stand next to the church?*
Answers on page 64

## Jill Howard-Jones

S.B. Publications

By the same author
*Secret Hereford*
*A Herefordshire Quiz Book*
*A Cambridgeshire Quiz Book*


*For Ray, Peter and Paul.*


First published in 1998 by S. B. Publications,
c/o 19 Grove Road, Seaford, East Sussex BN25 1TP

ISBN 1 85770 172 0


Designed and typeset by CGB, Lewes
Printed by Island Press
3 Cradle Hill Industrial Estate, Seaford, East Sussex BN25 3JE
Tel: 01323 490222

# CONTENTS

# INTRODUCTION

FOR me, Suffolk will always conjure idyllic memories of summer holidays when we used to escape from the industrial Midlands to Nayland Vicarage for a glorious month. My husband, a hospital chaplain, acted as the vicar's locum, while our small sons were employed in looking after the hens, romping with the vicar's endearingly boisterous Dalmatian in the fields adjoining the vicarage and fishing in the nearby pond. It was, and thankfully is still a predominantly pastoral county with church spires and windmills prickling dimpled fields.

I feel I know Suffolk but how well do you or I, whether inhabitant or visitor, really know it? Not well enough I suspect to answer all the questions in this book. That is why I have worded most in such a way that they can be entertainingly guessed while being at the same time unobtrusively informative.

Who passed through Ipswich on his way to London in 1800 and stayed with Lady Hamilton at the Great White Horse?' should call to mind that colourful lady's partner.

The 1420 inn that `gazes reverently down' on Lavenham could well suggest the Angel to anyone without a previous knowledge of the pubs of Lavenham's . . . but beware, the Well House in Framlingham does not necessarily take its name from the well. . .

I hope this quiz book will entertain families and groups in addition to the individual reader, with its competitive rounds, which may be chosen at random.

Answers at the back may be quickly found.

It has been fun to write. I hope it will be fun to read.

**Jill Howard-Jones**
**Autumn 1998.**

# 1 RECORDS

*One of the greatest archaeological discoveries ever made in the British Isles was at Sutton Hoo, near Woodbridge. There, in the summers of 1938 and 1939, an Anglo-Saxon ship burial containing a profusion of treasure, was discovered.*

1 Why are Pakenham's mills unique?

2 What natural disaster did Suffolk share with Essex on April 22, 1884?

3 Which is allegedly the most haunted rectory on the books of the Church of England?

4 Dennington Church's pyx canopy is probably the only one in England and one of only two in Europe. What is the pyx?

5 What record does the dovecote at Pond House, Polstead hold?

6 What does Constable's unique altarpiece in the church at Nayland feature?

7 The Suffolk Punch is the oldest of its kind in the world– but what is a Suffolk Punch?

8 The largest land formation of this sort in Europe is at Orford. What is it?

9 What is the Slaughden Redoubt and what record does it hold?

10 Gardeners had reason to be grateful when the first one in the world went into production in Ipswich in 1832.

# 2 MEN OF NOTE

*A good soft pillow for that good white head*
*Were better than a churlish turf in France.*

Shakespeare's *Henry V*. The king at
Agincourt to Sir Thomas Erpingham who
married Sir William of Clopton's daughter.

1 Which famous composer lived at
Snape windmill and started a music
festival there in 1947, before moving
to Crabbe St Aldeburgh?

2 Who passed through Ipswich on his way to London in November
1800 and stayed with Lady Hamilton at the Great White Horse?

3 Name the brother of architect Sir Christopher who witnessed the
Battle of Sole Bay and sent his own report to Whitehall.

4 This son of an Ipswich butcher was the cardinal who organised
Henry VIII's divorce from Catherine of Aragon. Who was he?

5 To which prince, much mourned by his widow, is Suffolk's
Framlingham College a memorial?

6 For what was Sir Alfred Munnings, born at the Mill House in
Mendham, famous?

7 What unwelcome news did Sir Henry Bunbury of Great Barton
break to Napoleon who pleaded: 'Let me be put in a country
house in the centre of England'?

8 Name the champion of slaves who is buried at Playford?

9 Thomas Cavendish of Trimley was second only to Sir Francis
Drake. What did he do?

10 What is Groton's connection with Massachusetts?

# 3 WOMEN OF NOTE

*Taste is the feminine of genius*
Edward Fitzgerald to J R Lowell.
October 1877

1 What was Jane Walker's contribution to medical science that led to the hospital at Wissington bearing her name?

2 'For God's sake don't, madam. I shouldn't know where to put them or what to do with them,' was George Borrow's response to Agnes Strickland. To what was he referring?

3 Elizabeth Garrett Anderson, the first woman mayor of Aldeburgh, was also the first woman in a distinguished profession. Which?

4 Her son recruited by telling young men that their country needed them in the First World War. She was born Anne Chevalier in Aspall. What was her married name?

5 Catherine Suckling, born at Barsham, was another mother of a famous son who became England's hero in 1805. Name him?

6 Which queen was entertained in Redgrave Hall by Sir Nicholas and Lady Bacon?

7 Who received the village of Cookley as part of her reward for agreeing to divorce the king?

8 Theodosia, Lady Adair, rebuilt Flixton Church in 1856. What does the church now contain in memory of her?

9 Who has given her name to a house in Palace Street, Newmarket where she reputedly stayed when Charles II brought the royal court to the town?

10 Eliza Mee of Bramford Church played its first organ for thirty five years and led the choir in spite of being disabled from birth. What disadvantage did she overcome?

# 4 CASTLES AND STATELY HOMES

*Lo, an English mansion founded*
*In the elder James's reign,*
*Quaint and stately and surrounded*
*With a pastoral domain.*
Edward Fitzgerald of Bredfield House,
where he was born.

1 The National Trust describe it as one of the largest and most beautiful of Suffolk's timber-framed farmhouses. It was once the home of the Umfreville family and is now occupied by novelist Nicholas Wollaston.

2 What happened to the Tudor mansion at Assington, the ancient seat of the Gurdon family in 1957?

3 Which sixteenth century royal residence is thought to have influenced Sir Thomas Kytson when he built the magnificent early Tudor mansion Hengrave Hall ?

4 How many towers are linked by the wall-walk around Framlingham Castle ?

5 Which castle, with a 90ft high keep, offers fine views across the River Ore.

6 There are very few manor houses like Little Wenham Hall in Britain. What is its distinguishing feature?

7 To which town was Christchurch Mansion presented by Felix Thornley Cobbold in 1896 ?

8 This ancestral hall and village in which it stands takes its name from the first Bishop of East Anglia.

9 Rushbrooke Hall is proud of its drawing room and furniture used in 1578 for a royal occasion. What happened there then?

10 Thetford Warren lodge was built in the early fifteenth century. Why?

# 5 ART AND CRAFTS

*I should paint my own places best.
Painting is but another word for
feeling. I associate my 'careless boyhood'
to all that lies on the banks
of the Stour.*
Constable.

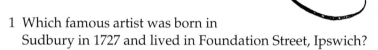

1 Which famous artist was born in
  Sudbury in 1727 and lived in Foundation Street, Ipswich?

2 Which artist made Flatford Mill famous?

3 What is still woven in Sudbury?

4 What operates at varying times in Woodbridge because it is
  dependent on the tide? It is also one of the most photographed
  scenes in England.

5 With which natural fibre are Lindsey and Kersey associated?

6 Which relative has Constable allegedly incorporated in his altar
  piece in Nayland Church ?

7 It is in Woodbridge, has six storeys and has got its sails back. What
  is it?

8 *Madonna and Child* in Barham Church is a Second World War
  memorial. By which famous sculptor?

9 William Hoare, RA, appropriately first 'saw' beauty when he
  lived in this town.

10 What is the connection between John Day, born 1522, of Little
   Bradley and Anglo-Saxon lettering?

# 6 INNS

*November 8th 1800. Lord Nelson, with Lady Hamilton, passed through Ipswich on his way to London. They stopped at the Great White Horse.*

1 Why is the Great White Hart at Scole said to be blessed by St Vincent?

2 What cruel entertainment was pursued at the Cock and Pye in Ipswich?

3 The name of this Sudbury inn might well be considered racist today.

4 The Wars of the Roses would seem to have left their mark on these two inns at opposite ends of Lindsey village. What are they called?

5 This Southwold Inn is reported to have flashed its lights to warn smugglers at sea . . . despite its connection with an illustrious admiral. Name him and the inn.

6 What legal distinction is claimed by the Ship at Dunwich?

7 What happened to the Three Marshes Inn at Slaughden in 1900?

8 The Parrot and Punchbowl is one of the oldest inns in Suffolk. In which century was it built?

9 Name the large 1420 inn which gazes reverently down on the Guildhall and Market Cross in Lavenham.

10 Bury St Edmunds boasts the smallest pub in Britain according to the *Guiness Book of Records*. Its name reflects its size – so what is it called?

# 7 FOR ALL THE SAINTS

*Traveller, I will relate a wonderous thing.
On the day on which Thomas Carter
breathed his last, a Sudbury camel passed
through the eye of a needle; if thou hast
wealth, go and do thou likewise.*

Inscription of 1706 in St Gregory's Church,
Sudbury.

1 'Here lies the Daye that darkness
could not blynd,' reads the
inscription on the gravestone at
Little Bradley, of the first English
printer to use Anglo-Saxon lettering. What was his name?

2 This saint's day was ushered in with the ringing of bells at St
Mary's church tower, Ipswich on April 23 1824.

3 A descendant of the founder of Gifford Hall, Thomas Heigham
lies in Gifford Church. He was a 'worthy and well-deserving
soldier,' so where does his hand rest?

4 The Protestant rector of Hadleigh was martyred in Mary Tudor's
reign. How and where did he die?

5 Name the first bishop of East Anglia who became a saint.

6 The only church in England dedicated to this saint is at
Whepstead. What is her name?

7 John Lowe, vicar of Brandeston for fifty years, was compelled to
read his own burial service. Why was he hanged?

8 Who is the most famous East Anglian saint, king and martyr,
killed by the Danes in 870 AD?

9 What part of Archbishop Simon Tybald's anatomy is on display
in the vestry of St Gregory's Church, Sudbury?

10 Who is the patron saint of pigs and much respected in Suffolk?

# 8 FLOWERS AND TREES

*Come to thy native groves and fruitful fields!*
*Thou knowest the fragrance that the wild*
*flower yields;*
*Inhale the breeze that bends the purple bud*
*And play along the margin of the wood.*

Robert Blomfield.

1  Why, according to legend, will primroses not grow in Cockfield?

2  Name the bush popularly known as 'Christmas' in Suffolk.

3  Plantations of these 'matchstick' trees were destroyed in Suffolk by the hurricane in October 1987.

4  Why was a rose brought from Persia and planted on Edward Fitzgerald's grave in Boulge churchyard?

5  This wood beside Dalham Hall would seem to suggest haberdashery

6  Can you name one or more of the coastal forests featured in the Tourist Information Centres' Three Forest Trail?

7  'Snowball' and 'Dumplin' are popular names in Suffolk for this flower.

8  Which well known wild flower was known as both 'Livelong' and 'Piss bed'?

9  Gifford's Hall at Hartest, Arger Fen at Assington, Appleby Garden in the abbey gardens at Bury St Edmunds and Ickworth Park at Horinger are known for their displays of flowers. Which is associated with a) daffodils, b) sweet peas, c) bluebells and d) roses?

10  Oxlips flourish in this wood at Cockfield, in a wood with similar bestial connections.

# 9 WRITERS

*How sharp the feeling of this Suffolk
seaboard country; spring coming all
in a rush, blossom spreading over it like
a great splash of foam.*

*Apple Acre* by Adrian Bell

1 Which novelist, author of *Lavengro*, lived near Lowesoft and was frequently seen walking the Suffolk lanes in his Spanish cloak and broad-brimmed hat?

2 For what kind of stories is M R James, also author of *Norfolk and Suffolk*, known, which are arguably the finest in the English language?

3 Which seaside town was used by Wilkie Collins as one of the settings for his novel *No Name*?

4 Although he did not like living in Southwold, living conditions cannot have been as bad as those he described in *1984*. Who was he?

5 What kind of writing made Richard Hakluyt, Rector of Wetheringsett, famous?

6 Who created Inspector Wexford and lives in Polstead?

7 What was the chief occupation of Adrian Bell, author of *Apple Acre, Corduroy, Silver Ley* and *The Cherry Tree?*

8 Which of Dickens's novels features Blundeston as the childhood home of his hero?

9 Who is not only the father of the English novel , but also the father of Nancy, the youngest of his twelve children buried at Stratford St Mary?

10 Bradfield Combust was Arthur Young's village. What subject did his writings mainly concern?

# 10 TOWNS OF WEST AND MID SUFFOLK

*A handsome little town, of thriving and cleanly appearance.*

Charles Dickens of Bury St Edmunds.

1  Who, during the eighteenth century, would ride on horseback through Bury St Edmunds, accompanied by the music of drums and flutes, to celebrate the Feast of St Crispin ?

2  Which building is pictured on Hadleigh's town sign, visible at either end of the bypass?

3  Which town was formerly known as Beaduricesworth (after an unknown settler Beaduric) before it became recognised as a saint's burial place?

4  Name the picturesque town with many timber-framed buildings made rich by the medieval wool trade, which lies about ten miles south of Bury St Edmunds.

5  Where in West Suffolk can you find a thousand kneelers?

6  Which small Suffolk town has been named for its clear water?

7  Which large Suffolk town is nicknamed `the Cradle of the Law' ? And why?

8  In Bury St Edmunds, one leads into the ruins of one of the richest monasteries in East Anglia, the other houses the bells for the cathedral church. What are they?

9  This town at the south western tip of Suffolk has its arts centre in the town hall and a popular East Town park.

10  Enjoying royal patronage in Suffolk, but surrounded by Cambridgeshire and a mere twenty minute drive from Cambridge.

# 11 TOWNS OF EAST SUFFOLK

*Beccles for a Puritan, Bungay for the poor,*
*Halesworth for a drunkard and Bilburgh*
*for a whore.*
Old saying.

1 Its name means 'old fort' and it has a museum in its Moot Hall.

2 The north part of which town stands on the island of Lothingland, completely encircled by water?

3 Dazzling white, stumpy and almost certainly the first thing you see in Southwold. What is it?

4 This was the former capital of East Anglia , a prosperous port with fifty two churches – all destroyed by the sea.

5 Leiston's Museum, one of the first production line engineering halls in the world, is more like an extended store . . . so what is it called?

6 Which Suffolk port is said to be named after the first Bishop of East Anglia?

7 You pronounce it Worbelswick, but how do you spell it?

8 Said to be the first new town to be built by the Angles, around 600AD, after their conquest of this part of Britain.

9 Which town is known as the 'garden resort of the east coast' with a seafront more than four miles long?

10 What stands at the north end of Lowestoft's High Street, gleaming beside its keeper's house ?

# 12 VILLAGES

*Benhall! Although I have not lately sought,*
*As I had purposed, thy delightful shades,*
*Their charms survive, and oft by memory's aids*
*In living beauty are before me brought.*

Bernard Barton.

1 This village, well known to Ruth Rendell, is where Maria Marten is said to have been murdered in the Red Barn.

2 What do Rickinhall Inferior, Botesdale and Rickinhall Superior have in common?

3 Dalham is a picturesque village characterised by its roofs. What is distinctive about them?

4 Its name has nothing to do with livers but probably derives from *Laefer* or irises around and in its great lake.

5 Which village means `a place of pools'?

6 What do the letters N E C stand for on certain houses in Eriswell near Mildenhall ?

7 Half in Essex, half in Suffolk, this village has a narrow bridge over the Stour and a wooden effigy of St Edmund in its church.

8 Name the area between Grundisburgh's church and pub which provides a focal point for the village.

9 Two buildings dominate the village of Freston. One is the Lode, what is the other?

10 Hoxne is known as King Edmund's village – but what is supposed to have happened to him here?

# 13 ROYALTY

*Her pure and eloquent blood*
*Spoke in her cheeks and so distinctly*
*wrought*
*That one might say her body thought.*

John Donne of Elizabeth Drury, age sixteen, loved
by Prince Henry, Charles Stuart's brother and
buried in Hawstead Church.

1  Which king came to the throne
   when the Great Stone on Hartest
   Green was removed from High
   Field, Somerton, on a sledge drawn by forty five horses?

2  Which member of the present royal family had silk for her
   wedding dress made in Sudbury?

3  King Edmund of East Anglia was said to have been hiding from
   the Danes under a hedge at Hoxne, before he was slain in 870. But
   what gave him away?

4  Who was staying at Framlingham Castle in 1553, when she learnt
   that she had become Queen?

5  Why did Henry II build Orford Castle?

6  Which king granted a charter to Ipswich in 1200, confirming the
   townsfolk's rights to administer their own affairs?

7  Which part of Anne Boleyn is said to be buried in Erwarton church?

8  How old was Edmund when he was crowned king of East Anglia
   in 855?

9  Which king was crowned by Simon of Sudbury, Archbishop of
   Canterbury in 1377?

10 Name the famous burial ground of the Anglo-Saxon kings of East
   Anglia near Woodbridge.

# 14 CHURCHES

*There is nothing half so green that I know anywhere, as the grass of that churchyard; nothing half so shady as its trees; nothing half so quiet as its tombstones.*

Charles Dickens of Blundeston.

1  Which tree was traditionally used to decorate St Mary's, Reydon on Whitsunday?

2  St Mary's the Virgin stands in the park of Edwardstone Hall, although the great house has now gone, leaving a red brick archway with lodge attached standing at the entrance now only to the church in the park. What is this entrance appropriately called?

3  What is strange about the carving of an angel in St Peter's church, Sudbury?

4  What unusual external feature does St Mary's church, Woolpit possess?

5  What part of St Andrews, Covehithe, which is north of Southwold and south of Benacre Broad, is visible from the sea?

6  Who was allegedly crowned on the site of the chapel barn in Bures on Christmas Day, 855?

7  It stands in East Bergholt churchyard– it is low, square and timber and its inhabitants weigh more than four tons. What is it ?

8  St Andrew's church tower in Walberswick was a suitable landmark for sailors, but what did the townsfolk use it for?

9  What unusual characteristic is shared by Bramfield and Beccles' church towers?

10  Although each has its own nave and chancel, what do Pakefield's two churches share?

# 15 CRIME AND PUNISHMENT

*The roaring boys of Pakefield*
*Didn't know what to contrive,*
*They had but one parson,*
*And him they buried alive.*

Old rhyme

1  Name the gang responsible for the fight at the Green Man, Ipswich on December 12 1778 and the murder of the master of the Ram Inn who interfered, perhaps on behalf of those unwilling to join the navy.

2  Who was hanged in public at Bury St Edmunds in 1930?

3  What kind of lawbreaker frequented the Three Mariners' Inn at Slaughden in the sixteenth century?

4  'The most arch act of piteous massacre that ever yet this land was guilty of' was, according to Shakespeare, carried out by Sir James Tyrrell of Gipping in the reign of Richard III. What did he do?

5  Which lane in Sudbury was unpopular with prisoners?

6  What was the charge levelled at the unnamed boy buried at a crossroads on the main Bury St Edmunds road near Kentford?

7  Who were ducked in the pond near Framlingham Castle in the seventeenth century?

8  What did Simon of Sudbury, Archbishop of Canterbury do to anger the peasants in 1381? And how was he punished?

9  What remains of the 1803 gaol at Bury St Edmunds?

10 Who seized King Edmund, bound him fast with chains, lacerated him with whips before their arrows slew him and they cut off his head?

# 16 DIALECT AND SAYINGS

*When yew lah an egg, tho' t'be a' gourd, don't cackle!*
Old saying

1 A 'pickcheese' is a bird, but which one and why is it so called?

2 What is the Fen nightingale?

3 Known as the 'temple' in Stoke-by-Nayland, but what is it really?

4 What are the Boxford Fleece and the Groton Fox?

5 'Sieve and Swillmaker' said a sign over the doorway of a Lowestoft house. What is a 'swill'?

6 Which animals are sometimes described as 'Widdles' and 'Diddles'?

7 The Froize Inn at Chillesford on the B1084, would presumably have done a good trade on Shrove Tuesday, so what is a `Froize'?

8 'Thass a nasty roke com'oova ta maashes'. Who or what is a 'roke'?

9 What is a Peterman?

10 Hanns in Norfolk, ails in Essex but in Suffolk they are awms. Interpret, please.

# 17 ROAD, RAIL AND RIVER

*Afoot and lighthearted I take to the road,*
*Healthy, free, the world before me,*
*The long brown path before me leading wherever I choose.*

Song of the Open Road. Walt Whitman.

1  A road in Lavenham of the female gender.

2  Name three Suffolk rivers with the names of birds?

3  Which 'sparkling' river rises near Rede and flows into the Stour south of the village to which it gives its name?

4  What name does the river Alde assume at Orford?

5  On the banks of which river does Woodbridge stand ?

6  Where is the most photographed section of the River Stour ?

7  What was permanently limited to 16 mph and showed a loss in 1928 when the first motor omnibuses entered Southwold to pick up passengers?

8  Why is Double Street in Framlingham so named ?

9  This river's name implies its age!

10  What is the Box?

# 18 POETS

*We in this Suffolk are not so completely given
over to prose and turnips as some would have us.
I have always said that being near the sea, and
being able to catch a glimpse of it from the
tops of the hills and of houses, redeemed
Suffolk from dullness. . .*

Edward Fitzgerald.

1  Who was Suffolk's nature poet, born on December 3 1766 at Honnington?

2  Which part of his long epic poem, *The Seasons*, did James Thomson write in Stradishall in 1726?

3  Which poet translated the *Rubaiyat of Omar Khayam* from Persian into English, was born at Bredfield House in 1809 , lived most of his life in a cottage on the Boulge Hall estate and  never left Suffolk in all his seventy four years?

4  Which famous playwright's company played at Ipswich in 1595?

5  Who was born on Christmas Eve 1754 in Aldeburgh and became not only both a qualified surgeon and local curate but also a famous poet?

6  He satirised the merchants of Ipswich in his *Canterbury Tales.*

7  Marjorie Wilson, the rector of Blaxhall's daughter, wrote poems which especially appealed to children . Which newspaper published them?

8  Bearing the name of another county although his father was the Duke of Norfolk, he is known for introducing blank verse into English poetry.

9  Which young poet came to Thorney Hall, Stowmarket to visit his old tutor and  later wrote *Paradise Lost?*

10  What did William Broome, rector of Stuston,  translate – which the poet, Alexander Pope, used to advantage?

# 19 MILITARY MATTERS

*The riflemen are coming*
*From Hadleigh and from Eye,*
*From Sudbury and Mildenhall,*
*From places far and nigh,*
*Stowmarket, Brandon, Wickham brook,*
*Brave hearts and true draw near,*
*Ring out, ring out blithe Bury bells,*
*And greet each volunteer.*

Old rhyme

1  Which regiment were the bells of Bury St Edmunds welcoming in June 1861?

2  For defence from which enemy were the round Martello towers built between Felixstowe and Aldeburgh?

3  Orford Ness was a secret military site and occupied by RAF and Atomic Weapons' Researchers. What is it known for now?

4  Who fought the English in the Battle of Sole Bay (off Southwold town) in 1672?

5  This legless pilot flew with the RAF from Martlesham Heath near Woodbridge in the Second World War.

6  The site of eight cannons on this hill at Southwold gives it its name.

7  How did Ipswich barges become involved in the Second World War in 1940?

8  Where in Suffolk is the largest military air display in the world held?

9  In which war did Colonel Grissell of the Coldstream Guards from Redisham Hall, Ringsfield fight?

10  A young soldier called Jack the Smiter is a popular figure in Southwold. Where can you find him and what does he do?

# 20 CREATURES

*Round Euston's watered vale and
sloping plains;
Where woods and groves in solemn
grandeur rise;
Where the kite brooding unmolested flies;
The woodcock and the painted pheasant race,
And skulking foxes destined for the chase.*

Robert Bloomfield.

1 What, according to an old Suffolk saying: 'In April shakes his bill, in May pipes all day, in June changes his tune, flies away in July and must away in August'?

2 A total of 1,418 of these creatures were caught at Woodton Hall by William Hunt of Wood Rising in 1759.

3 Where is the Suffolk Horse Museum?

4 Who was Snooks, whose statue stands by the Yacht Pond in Aldeburgh?

5 Which night creature appears to have given its name to a Suffolk river?

6 Emblem of the RSPB, this bird returned to nest on Havergate Island in 1947.

7 How does a large stag's head provide amusement at the White Horse Inn in Sweffling?

8 Which animals form the Suffolk Trinity, the basis of the county's agricultural history?

9 What is Cow Wise?

10 Name the famous horse of children's fiction connected with Sutton because Anna Sewell's mother was born there.

# 21 FOOD AND DRINK

*Here with a loaf of bread beneath the bough,*
*A Flask of Wine, a Book of Verse and Thou. . .*

The Rubaiyat of Omar Khayyam.
Edward Fitzgerald.

1  The fish market at Southwold was housed in a round building with a suitable name. What was it called?

2  What was the 'grog' which Admiral Edward Vernon of Orwell Park used to give to his sailors?

3  What commodity was vital to the fishing industry before refrigeration and how was it obtained?

4  What are Suffolk smokies?

5  What were St Anthony's turnips?

6  Which town's Cucumber Society became famous for its show in the mid nineteenth century?

7  What is the Polstead Black?

8  Where can you find the following list inscribed in Aldeburgh: 'Crabbe, Carp, Pike, Sammon, Shrimp, Spratte, Turbette, Wale and Whiting'?

9  In Suffolk Whit Sunday was celebrated with baked custards and pies made of which fruit?

10  What did Cobbolds start at Cliff Quay, Ipswich in 1746, using water from Holywells?

# 22 ACCIDENTS AND APPARITIONS

*No goblin he, no imp of sin*
*No crimes has ever known;*
*They took the shaggy stranger in*
*And reared him as their own.*

Robert Bloomfield

1  A former rector of Polstead haunts his parish by driving round it in a carriage, but it is his horse that disturbs those who sight the spectre. Why?

2  In July 1804, Thomas Cutting, servant to Mr Porter of Felixstowe was covering a stack of clover to keep it from the rain – an activity which proved fatal. Why?

3  What was sixty feet high, built in the twelfth century, had five bells but fell down on December 29 1883?

4  Who or what was Old Shuck, responsible for killing several people in Bungay's parish church after suddenly appearing in a thunderstorm?

5  What happened to 'Black Toby' at the junction of the B1387 and A12?

6  What does a Suffolk long house lack, which might suggest faulty design?

7  What destroyed most of Southwold in 1659?

8  Beside St James's Church, Dunwich stand the ruins of an ancient colony for those who unfortunately contracted a certain disease. What did they suffer from?

9  Why are horses said to hate passing Reydon Hall on the road between Southwold and Wangford?

10  What crime did William Corder commit which caused him to allegedly haunt Cock Farm which faces Polstead Green?

# 23 TRADITION AND FOLKLORE

*All down the church in midst of fire*
*The hellish monster flew;*
*And passing onward to the choir*
*He many people slew.*

Of the devil in the form of a black dog
who swept through St Mary's church,
Bungay in the violent thunderstorm
of 1577.

1 What did it mean if the first foal of the year stood up facing the farmer ?

2 What were three herons flying together from east to west supposed to indicate?

3 What is water from the Lady's Well at Woolpit said to cure?

4 Who, according to local tradition was fished out of the sea at Leiston in the thirteenth century and refused to speak so he could not be converted to Christianity?

5 Where do the bells of fifty two lost churches allegedly ring under the sea?

6 What happens after the ringing of the eight o'clock bell on Sunday morning at Freckenham?

7 What was the traditional farmhouse reward for a servant who could bring in a branch of hawthorn in full bloom in May?

8 What did they celebrate in old Suffolk on October 11 instead of on September 29?

9 Who is Southwold Jack and what gets him going?

10 What was the Reader who lived in the Readery at Framlingham, instructed to read every day to the inhabitants of the almhouses?

# 24 MISCELLANEOUS

*The game is never lost till won.*
*Gretna Green* by George Crabbe 1754-1832.

1 What did Tom Paddock win in 1856 near Bentley, Suffolk after fifty one rounds?

2 How many Thoringtons are there in Suffolk?

3 What office is held by the Right Reverend Richard Lewis in the diocese of St Edmundsbury and Ipswich?

4 What can you view from the John Bradfield Viewing Area?

5 Which Ipswich Club started as an amateur side in 1878?

6 How did Well Close Square, Framlingham get its name?

7 Which town on the western borders of Suffolk is famous for horse racing?

8 Mildenhall was the starting point of an air race in 1934. Where were the two pilots going and why was their feat significant?

9 Situated near Leiston, this place is known for its nuclear power stations.

10 Where was the centre of power in Suffolk for 500 years?

# 25 SUFFOLK BY THE SEA

*Here is a glorious City in the Sea,*
*The sea is in the broad, the narrow streets,*
*Ebbing and flowing . . .*

Samuel Rogers

1  When the fishermen's church at Pakefield was rebuilt in 1950 – it had been destroyed by enemy action in 1941 – it had the same type of roof as the original. What was that?

2  On September 24 1879 the nine mile rail link from Southwold to Walberswick opened. In what year did it close?

3  Name the king who, in 1215, gave Dunwich its first charter?

4  Old Dunwich has disappeared beneath the sea. By what name did the Romans know it?

5  Where, near Kessingland, will you find monkeys, llamas, lions, tigers and many varieties of exotic birds?

6  Who was the German empress who made Felixstowe fashionable?

7  And in which century did she first visit the resort with her children?

8  In Georgian times this sea port was known for the production of soft paste porcelain, similar to that made at Worcester. Name the port and the porcelain.

9  Suffolk beachcombers occasionally find amber and, more often, a flesh coloured semi-precious stone. What is it?

10  The Suffolk coast has suffered from attacks by the sea. The most recent devastation by flooding was after the Second World War. In what year?

# 26 ALL ABOUT BRECKLAND

*The Walrus and the Carpenter*
*Were walking close at hand:*
*They wept like anything to see*
*Such quantities of sand:*
*'If this was only cleared away,'*
*They said, 'it* would *be grand!'*

Lewis Carroll

1  Name the Victorian authority on the area – he knew its every stick, stone and creature – who gave Breckland its name?

2  And what was the title of the book in which he introduced the name?

3  What is the name of the prehistoric track, much improved by the Romans, that entered Breckland at Cavenham. It was the only path that linked this water bounded county with the rest of Britain.

4  Who was the Sikh prince who bought an estate at Barnham Common in 1863, built Elvendon Hall and adopted the lifestyle of an English country gentleman.

5  He added a jewel to the British Crown. Which one?

6  Who later bought the estate and turned it into the largest farm in all England?

7  Brandon was once famed for one of the most ancient crafts of England. What was it?

8  What was planted in Breckland in 1922 that has changed the appearance of a wide area of its land?

9  Suffolk shares the 400 or so square miles of Breckland with Norfolk. Which county has the greater acreage?

10  This is the largest parish in the county, and gives its name to a treasure horde of Roman silver plate, now in the British Museum.

# 27 FORTS, FIGHTS, AND LIGHTS

*Anythin' for a quiet life, as the man said wen he took the sitivation at the lighthouse.*

Sam Weller in *Pickwick Papers* by Charles Dickens

1 When a brick and stone lighthouse was built in 1676 at Lowestoft a plaque on it bore the name of the then Secretary to the Admiralty – who perhaps noted the event in his diary. His name?

2 There were four other seamarks built along the Suffolk coast. Name any two of them.

3 Coastal defences included a number of martello towers. From whence was the name of these defences derived?

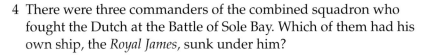

4 There were three commanders of the combined squadron who fought the Dutch at the Battle of Sole Bay. Which of them had his own ship, the *Royal James*, sunk under him?

5 What was the result?

6 Who built the great fort of Burgh Castle?

7 What was the appropriately named fort built in the early seventeenth century to safeguard Harwich?

8 One of the governors of a later fort on the same site commissioned a youthful artist to sketch it for him. Who was the artist?

9 James Wolfe, an ensign of the Twelfth, carried the colours of this famous Suffolk regiment at a parade at Blackheath in 1742. He went on to make history in a siege in a city across the sea. Which one?

10 What was the nickname of the old Twelfth, which later became the Suffolk Regiment?

# 28 INVENTORS AND INVENTIONS

*God hath made man upright; but they have sought out many inventions.*

Ecclesiastes 7.29

1 What emergency treatment of blood loss was invented by W H Williams, a Doctor of Medicine who settled in Ipswich in 1801?

2 After producing the first lawn mower Charles May and Robert Ransome turned their attention to railway construction. What did they produce in this field in 1832?

3 The discovery of coprolites in East Suffolk helped in the development of scientific farming. Into what where they converted by the firm of Packard, Chapman and Fison?

4 And what are coprolites?

5 What was the advantage of Ransome's cast iron ploughshare, patented in 1803, over the steel share then in use?

6 The firm of W A and A C Churchman was founded at Ipswich in 1790. What did it produce?

7 In Bury St Edmunds the lavanders lived near the South Gate. What did the lavanders do?

8 J Stringall of Ipswich invented an aid to agriculture known as a 'stringall'. What was a stringall?

9 The Reverend John Priestley, Congregational minister at Needham when a student, became a Greek scholar and a scientist. His discovery of what has helped millions to breathe more easily?

10 The Duke of York, later George VI, inaugurated a boys' camp here in the 1930s. He shared in all the life, but was allowed an iron bedstead in his tent rather than sleeping bag on the ground.

# SOUTH AND MID-SUFFOLK
# PICTURE QUIZ

**1**    What is the function of this building at Tattingstone?

**2**    Name this mill and the artist who made it famous.

On the seafront of which **3** town does this old Moot Hall stand?

**4** What is the name of this busy river estuary and bridge?

**5** This tower lies just south of the Ipswich bypass. Why did Lord Freston build it for his daughter?

**6** What and where is this building?

**7** What gruesome reminder of a hated archbishop can be found in this church?

8 What and where is this building and why is it unique?

**9** What is the artist painting?

10 Where is this figurehead and how does it link Suffolk with Greenwich?

# NORTH AND MID-SUFFOLK
# PICTURE QUIZ

**1** A well known building in Bury St Edmunds – but what is it?

**2**  Where is St Edmunds and what is striking about its roof?

**3**  Which town has a Double Street next to the church?

**4** Who – and where – is he?

**5** The seat of Suffolk's power and the residence of the Dukes of Norfolk for 500 years. Where is it?

**6** Beach huts on the promenade. Of which seaside resort?

7  What is this memorial bench in the Abbey Gardens, Bury St Edmunds made of – and why?

8  What is the name of the town, and the hill, where these cannons stand?

In the centre of which town is there a weathervane, featuring a black dog, on top of a lamp post?

**9**

**10** Why is Joseph the gipsy boy buried beside the main Bury St Edmunds to Newmarket road?

# ANSWERS

# 1 RECORDS

1  Pakenham is the last British village with a working windmill and watermill.

2  The Great Earthquake centring round Colchester caused vibrations which reached London in one direction and Ipswich and Sudbury in another.

3  Polstead Rectory, now the Old Rectory. The sound of carriage wheels, a smell suggesting fish and glue, a presence in the attic room and a voice calling 'John' have been reported.

4  A receptacle in which the Eucharistic Host is kept.

5  It is said to be the largest in the country.

6  The Last Supper.

7  The oldest breed of heavy working horses. The Suffolk Punch can be seen at work at Rede Hall Farm Park, near Bury St Edmunds, and at Kentwell Hall in Long Melford.

8  The strip of shingle or spit, which forms the peninsula known as Orford Ness.

9  It is the biggest and most northern round fort or martello tower along the English coast. It contains about a million bricks and can be viewed by appointment with the owners, the Landmark Trust.

10  The world's first lawnmower.

# 2 MEN OF NOTE

1  Benjamin Britten.

2  Lord Nelson.

3  Matthew Wren.

4  Cardinal Wolsey.

5  Prince Albert, husband of Queen Victoria.

6  His paintings.

7  When told that he was to be exiled for life on St Helena, Napoleon's response was: 'What am I to do on this little rock at the end of the world?'

8  Thomas Clarkson. He lived to eighty six  and died knowing that nowhere in the British Empire could slavery legally exist.

9  He was the second Englishman to sail round the world, reaching home in 1588, taking two years and fifty days.

10 Winthrop, the first Governor of Massachusetts came from Groton.

## 3 WOMEN OF NOTE

1  She pioneered the fresh air treatment for diseases of the lungs. The Jane Walker Hospital was once a tuberculosis sanatorium.

2  Her books – twelve volumes of her *Queens of England*.

3  She was the first woman doctor on the British Medical Register.

4  Kitchener. Anne Chevalier married Henry Kitchener in 1845.

5  Nelson.

6  Queen Elizabeth I.

7  Anne of Cleves, whom Henry VIII divorced.

8  A chapel – with a beautiful fan-vaulted roof and clustered columns.

9  Nell Gwynne.

10 She was blind from birth.

## 4 CASTLES AND STATELY HOMES

1  Thorington Hall.

2  It was burnt to the ground.

3  Hampton Court Palace. Hengrave Hall is complete with Queen's Chamber where Elizabeth I slept.

4  Thirteen.

5  Orford Castle. It has twenty steps to the door of the keep and ninety one more inside.

6  It is fortified – one of the rare thirteenth century small castellated houses.

7  Ipswich.

8  Flixton Hall. Flixton is named after St Felix.

9  Queen Elizabeth I visited the house with her train of retainers. The original hangings, on the bed in which she allegedly slept, remain.

10 This two-storey hunting lodge was built for the keeper of the large Westwick rabbit warren.

# 5 ART AND CRAFTS

1 Thomas Gainsborough. His first major commissions involved painting several local people in Ipswich.

2 Constable. His painting of Flatford Mill, in which his father lived, is famous.

3 Silk.

4 Tide Mill.

5 Wool.

6 His elder brother.

7 The windmill known as Buttrum's Mill.

8 Henry Moore.

9 Eye.

10 He was the first English printer to use it.

# 6 INNS

1 A splendid old vine adorned its walls; its small white grapes were turned into wine.

2 Cocking. A chain of cocks were fought during the races, between the gentlemen of Beccles and the gentlemen of Chelmsford.

3 The Black Boy Inn.

4 The White Rose and the Red.

5 (The) Lord Nelson.

6 Allegedly one of the first inns in England to be licensed.

7 It collapsed when a severe storm cut away the foreshore at Slaughden.

8 Sixteenth century. It dates back to at least 1591.

9 The Angel.

10 The Nutshell. The Smith's Arms in Godmanstone, Dorset, also lays claim to being the smallest pub in England.

# 7 FOR ALL THE SAINTS

1 John Day.

2 St. George, coinciding with the King's birthday, when cakes and wine were distributed.

3  On his sword and he is dressed in armour.

4  By burning – on Aldham Common. His commemorative obelisk can easily be seen from the road.

5  St Felix, who landed at Dunwich in 631 AD.

6  St Petronilla. She was an early Roman martyr, the date and details of whose death are unknown.

7  He was accused of witchcraft during the sixteenth century. The old sick parson was tortured until he gave way and confessed to employing two imps to sink ships at sea.

8  St Edmund.

9  His skull. The Archbishop was the Chancellor of the Exchequer in 1381, who by imposing the hated poll tax, initiated the Peasants' Revolt and was beheaded by the rebels under Wat Tyler,his head being returned to Sudbury where he was once bishop.

10  St Anthony.

# 8  FLOWERS AND TREES

1  When Cockfield was depopulated by the plague, primroses were believed to have also caught the infection and died.

2  Holly.

3  Poplars.

4  The rose originated from one growing on Omar Khayyam's grave in Persia, Edward Fitzgerald being famous for his imaginative free translation of *The Rubaiyat of Omar Khayyam*.

5  Bluebutton Wood.

6  Tangham, Tunstall and Dunwich.

7  The guelder rose.

8  Dandelion.

9  Daffodils at Ickworth Park, Horinger; sweet peas at Gifford's Hall, Hartest; bluebells at Arger Fen, Assington and roses in the Appleby Rose Garden, Bury St Edmunds.

10  Bulls Wood.

# 9 WRITERS

1  George Borrow.
2  Ghost stories.
3  Aldeburgh (called Aldborough in the novel).
4  George Orwell.
5  Travel. His famous work is *Navigations, Voyages, Traffiques and Discoveries of the English Nation by Sea or Overland.*
6  Ruth Rendell.
7  He was a Suffolk farmer.
8  *David Copperfield.*
9  Samuel  Richardson, author of *Pamela, Clarissa* and *Sir Charles Grandison.*
10  Agriculture, but his most famous work described his travels in France and outlined the causes of the French Revolution.

## 10 TOWNS OF WEST AND MID SUFFOLK

1  The shoemakers.
2  The gatehouse known as Pykenham's Tower.
3  Bury St Edmunds.
4  Lavenham.
5  In the Cathedral Church of St James, Bury St Edmunds.
6  Clare, at the head of the River Stow.
7  Bury St Edmunds because the barons swore an oath in 1214 in the abbey to force King John to sign the Magna Carta, which he later did at Runnymede in Surrey.
8  The two gateways into the old city.
9  Haverhill.
10  Newmarket , where horseracing has enjoyed royal patronage since 1605.

## 11 TOWNS OF EAST SUFFFOLK

1  Aldeburgh or Ealdeburgh.
2  Lowestoft.
3  The lighthouse. Its beacon is still in use but it is not open to the public.

4 Dunwich. Its museum contains a model of how it was in its former glory as a large medieval town.

5 The Long Shop Museum.

6 Felixstowe (after Bishop Felix).

7 WALBERSWICK.

8 Ipswich , situated at the lower crossing of the River Orwell.

9 Felixstowe.

10 The High Lighthouse, *circa* 1854.

## 12 VILLAGES

1 Polstead. Maria Marten was an ill-fated Victorian heroine.

2 The three villages all share one street.

3 Four out of five are thatched.

4 Livermere.

5 Polstead.

6 New England Company. The Eriswell estates were bought from money raised in the seventeenth century to send missionaries out to the North American Indians. The revenue from the estates was invested in the New England Company for the propagation of the Gospel in New England.

7 Bures.

8 The village green.

9 Freston Tower, a Tudor Suffolk skyscraper with six chambers.

10 The martyr king is believed to have been chained to a tree, whipped and pierced with arrows till he died.

## 13 ROYALTY

1 George I. August 1 st.1714.

2 The Princess Royal (Anne).

3 His shadow.

4 Mary Tudor.

5 For coastal defences and against invaders from the sea.

6  King John.

7  Her heart. The story is that after her execution at the Tower, her body was removed in a narrow chest by sympathisers who brought her heart to Ewarton, her uncle's home, for burial.

8  Only fifteen.

9  Richard II.

10  Sutton Hoo. It is open from mid April to the end of October.

## 14 CHURCHES

1  Birch boughs.

2  Temple Bar.

3  The angel has a beard.

4  It has a nineteenth century spire, despite it being a fifteenth century church.

5  The tower of this ruined church is visible from the sea.

6  St Edmund, the martyr-king of the East Angles was, according to a manuscript in the University Library at Cambridge, crowned here.

7  A unique wooden bell "cage", in which five bells are hung upside down and are rung by being pushed by hand.

8  A lookout for possible invaders.

9  Both towers are detached. Bramfield's is 20ft from the church, while Beccles' 97ft tower stands to the east of the church.

10  They share the same tower.

## 15 CRIME AND PUNISHMENT

1  The press gang.

2  No one. William Corder of Street Farm, Polstead , hanged for murder in 1829, was the last man to be hanged in public. An account of his crime was bound in his own skin.

3  Smugglers. Will Lund was a famous smuggler. The inn collapsed in 1900 in a severe storm.

4  He carried out the murder of the princes in the Tower.

5  Gaol Lane, passing through a restored gateway to the old town gaol.

6 This young shepherd was accused of sheep stealing. He hung himself, perhaps out of guilt and/or fear of transportation. Suicides were often buried at cross-roads to prevent the unhappy spirit from wandering.

7 Suspected witches. Many witch trials took place in Framlingham.

8 He re-introduced the hated poll tax, which the peasants could not pay. The Peasants' Revolt ensued. After breaking into the Tower and dragging him to Tower Hill they executed him there with eight blows of the axe.

9 The gatehouse and entrance wall.

10 The Danes. Edmund had reigned in peace by paying tribute to the Danes, who nevertheless broke into his kingdom. The brave king sacrificed himself to save his people.

## 16 DIALECT AND SAYINGS

1 Blue Tit. Cheese was the bait usually employed by a boy to bait his tit-trap.

2 The frog.

3 The Temple is thought to be a fishing lodge. This pavilion is all that survives of Sir John Soane's Tendring Hall.

4 Inns. It is customary to use the village name followed by the name of the inn in parts of Suffolk.

5 A 'swill' is a large basket into which the herrings were first put when landed from the boats.

6 'Widdles' are very young ducks, also referred to as 'Diddles', a term also applied to sucking pigs.

7 'Froize' is old Suffolk for a pancake.

8 A 'roke' is old Suffolk for a mist.

9 A fisherman.

10 They are all beards of barley.

## 17 ROAD, RAIL AND RIVER

1 Lady Street.

2 The Lark, Linnet and Dove.

3 The Gleme (Glemsford).

4  The Ore.

5  The Deben.

6  At Flatford Mill (between Manningtree and Dedham).

7  The Southwold Railway.

8  It was the first street in the country to have houses and shops on both sides.

9  River Alde, which took its name from the town Aldeburgh ('old borough')

10  A river, tributary of the Stour.

## 18 POETS

1  Robert Bloomfield.

2  The part called 'Winter.'

3  Edward Fitzgerald.

4  Shakespeare's.

5  George Crabbe.

6  Geoffrey Chaucer.

7  *The Children's Newspaper.*

8  Surrey.  Henry Howard, Earl of Surrey.

9  John Milton.

10  Homer's *Odyssey.* William Broome and his friend Elijah Fenton translated about half of it, which Pope found useful in his own acclaimed translation.

## 19  MILITARY MATTERS

1  The Suffolk Volunteer Rifle Corps, members of which first made their appearance in grey uniform at Bury St Edmunds in June 1861.

2  Napoleon and the French.

3  Its plant and bird life (access from Orford Quay).

4  The Dutch; not the French who were England's allies on this occasion.

5  Douglas Bader.

6  Gun Hill.

7  They were among the little ships that evacuated troops from Dunkirk.

8  Royal Air Force, Mildenhall.

9  The South African War, in which he won great distinction; and the Great War, in which he fell near Gaza.

10  At Southwold Church. Clothed in armour of about 1470, he strikes the hour bell, holding his sword in one hand and his battle-axe in the other.

## 20 CREATURES

1  The cuckoo.

2  Rats.

3  Woodbridge.

4  A dog, given in gratitude for the life of Dr Robin Acheson who with his wife, Dr Nora, founded the local medical practice.

5  The Bat.

6  The avocet.

7  In the old inn game of Ringing the Bull – the 'Bull' can be a stuffed stag's, bull's or ram's head – the player has to hook a metal ring suspended from the ceiling on a length of line on to the hook on the animal's nose.

8  The Red Poll cow, the Suffolk sheep and the Suffolk Punch, a handsome working horse.

9  A working dairy farm at Meadow Farm, West Stow.

10  Black Beauty, created by Anna Sewell. Anna's mother also wrote books for children.

## 21 FOOD AND DRINK

1  The Kipperdrome.

2  Rum ration watered down. His cloak of corded silk or grosgrain gave the name 'grog' to his second rate booze.

3  Salt. Rough salt was extracted from sea water by solar evaporation.

4  Pieces of smoked haddock in a creamy sauce, served with brown toast and butter.

5  The roots of the buttercup.

6  Ipswich.

7  A cherry – small, sweet and very dark.

8  In the church register – not at the fishmongers'. It is an indication that fishing has been the principal industry in Aldeburgh for many generations.

9  Gooseberries.

10  Their brewery. Tolly Cobbold is one of the finest Victorian breweries in the country.

## 22 ACCIDENTS AND APPARITIONS

1  The horse is headless.

2  Lightning struck him dead.

3  The church tower at Freckenham.

4  The phantom black dog of Bungay·

5  Black Toby, a negro drummer in the Dragoons was hanged for rape and murder and is said still to haunt the nearby picnic site known as Toby's Walks.

6  It has no corridor so you have to walk through all the other rooms to get to the room at the end.

7  Fire– not the sea, although a wind off the sea fanned the blaze which destroyed 238 houses, the town hall, gaol, market house and breweries.

8  Leprosy.

9  They are said to shy at the sight of four headless horses drawing a ghostly coach carrying the ghost of a wicked squire.  In the early twentieth century, a rider was killed when his horse shied at something invisible to humans.

10  He murdered his lover, the molecatcher's daughter. He is said to have spent his last night at Cock Farm before his arrest.

## 23 TRADITION AND FOLKLORE

1  Good luck – but if the foal's tail faced the farmer, it was bad luck.

2  Bad weather within twenty four hours.

3  Bad eyes.

4 A merman. In reality perhaps a walrus, but not a seal as they would have been familiar with seals.

5 Dunwich.

6 The day of the month is then tolled out. The custom appears to be very old and probably goes back to the days when very few households had a calendar.

7 A dish of cream for breakfast.

8 Old Michaelmas Day. September 29 is the Feast of St Michael and All Angels.

9 A model of a Wars of the Roses' soldier on the wall of St Edmund's church at Southwold. At the start of each service, a rope hanging from his waist is pulled by a sidesman which makes Jack strike a bell with the hammer in his right hand.

10 The Bible – by the terms of Robert Hitcham's will.

## 24 MISCELLANEOUS

1 Boxing's 'barefist championship of England' and £400.

2 Two. One in the northeast near Blythburgh, the other within the parish of Stoke.

3 He is the bishop of the diocese.

4 Felixstowe and Harwich shipping at close quarters.

5 Ipswich Football Club.

6 From Mr Henry Wells whose shop (1829) sold `everything'.

7 Newmarket.

8 Charles Scott and Campbell black flew from Mildenhall to Melbourne, Australia in just under seventeen hours. It was the fastest journey across the world then known.

9 Sizewell. It has an exhibition complex which is open from Easter to October.

10 Framlingham Castle, where the Dukes of Norfolk lived.

# 25 SUFFOLK BY THE SEA

1 It was thatched.

2 The last train ran in 1929 .

3 King John. The town paid 200 marks and 5,000 eels to the crown to be a free borough.

4 *Sitomagus.*

5 In the many acres of woodland of the Suffolk Wild Life Park.

6 The Empress Augusta, wife of Kaiser Wilhelm, Queen Victoria's grandson.

7 In 1891.

8 Lowestoft.

9 Cornelian.

10 The East Coast Floods Disaster was in 1953.

# 26 ALL ABOUT BRECKLAND

1 W G Clarke

2 *In Breckland Wilds.*

3 Ichnield Way.

4 Maharajah Duleep Singh.

5 The Koh-i-noor diamond.

6 Edward Cecil Guinness, the first Lord Iveagh, who also gave Kenwood House, with its fine collection of pictures, to the nation.

7 Flint knapping. Flint was mined, flaked and knapped in the area from Neolithic times.

8 The first state forest, which brought pines and firs to this area of heathland.

9 Norfolk. It has 253 square miles. There are 145 square miles in Suffolk.

10 Mildenhall, it occupies 17,000 acres.

# 27 FORTS, FIGHTS AND LIGHTS

1 Samuel Pepys
2 Orford Light, Landguard Light at Felixstowe, Pakefield Light and Bawdsey Light – demolished in 1924 because of coastal erosion.
3 Cape Mortello in Corsica.
4 James, Duke of York.
5 A draw. Losses on both sides were about equal when nightfall, and the onset of a thick fog, brought the battle to a close.
6 The Romans, in the third century.
7 Landguard. For a time it was one of the 230 saluting stations in Great Britain and could fly the Royal standard on royal anniversaries and State occasions.
8 Thomas Gainsborough.
9 As General James Wolfe he commanded the British forces in Canada at the siege of Quebec. He won a famous victory but it cost him his life.
10 The Swedebashers.

# 28 INVENTORS AND INVENTIONS

1 The field tourniquet. It was taken up by the Army Medical Board and issued to every regiment.
2 The first self-propelling steam engine.
3 Fertiliser.
4 The fossilised dung of flesh eating creatures.
5 It remained sharp in use.
6 Tobacco products, including cigarettes from around 1857.
7 They wash and prepare cloth before it is dyed.
8 An iron mushroom- shaped stand round which a hayrick is built.
9 Oxygen.
10 Southwold.

# 29 SOUTH AND MID SUFFOLK
## PICTURE QUIZ

1 Living accommodation. It is not a church but the false front of a row of cottages. The local squire built this folly, known as the Tattingstone Wonder, in the eighteenth century so that he could see a 'church' from his manor.

2 Flatford Mill, the subject of John Constable's famous painting.

3 Aldeburgh.

4 The River Orwell crossed by Orwell Bridge, which has the biggest single span of pre-stresssed concrete in England.

5 As a school for his daughter, Ellen. On the ground floor she was to study the practice of charity for one day a week; on the first floor she had to weave tapestries, study music on the second floor, read ancient languages on the third, English literature on the fourth, apply herself to painting on the fifth and study astrology on the sixth.

6 Lavenham. It is the Guildhall.

7 The skull of Simon Tybald, the Archbishop Chancellor beheaded by Wat Tyler's rebels in 1381 is in the vestry and can be seen by arrangement with the Vicar of St Gregory's in Sudbury.

8 The bell cage at East Bergholt, which holds the five heaviest bells in England.

9 The Tide Mill at Woodbridge.

10 The figurehead from HMS *Ganges* stands outside the Royal Hospital School at Holbrook. This boarding school for boys and girls aged 11-18, was founded in Greenwich, originally for children of seafarers. It moved to Holbrook in 1933 as the result of a generous local benefactor. The teak-built HMS *Ganges*, on which thousands of boys trained for sea was stationed at nearby Shotley Gate.

# 30 NORTH AND MID SUFFOLK
## PICTURE QUIZ

1 The Corn Exchange.

2 Southwold. The roof is bright green.

3 Framlingham

4 St Edmund, King and Martyr in the Abbey Gardens, Bury St Edmunds.

5 Framlingham Castle.

6 Southwold.

7 Metal, from the metal frame of an American Flying Fortress, commemorating American servicemen stationed nearby in the Second World War.

8 10 Gun Hill, Southwold.

9 Bungay. The Black Dog of Bungay, according to tradition, appeared in a thunderstorm and killed some of the parishioners in church.

10 He hanged himself after being accused of stealing sheep. It was believed that burying a suicide at a crossroads would prevent the unhappy spirit from wandering.

# LINE ILLUSTRATIONS ON RELATED SUBJECTS

*Quiz*

1 Sceptre from the Sutton Hoo ship burial.

2 Cardinal Wolsey.

3 Nell Gwynne.

4 Orford Castle.

6 Detail from a carved bracket on the Swan Inn, Clare.

7 St Augustine

10 Bear on the parapet of the church at Haverhill.

11 Bungay village sign.

12 Mildenhall's market cross.

13 Arms attributed to the martyred King Edmund.

*Quiz*

14 Bell cage of East Bergholt church.

17 Pack horse bridge at Moulton.

18 Geoffrey Chaucer.

19 Martello tower.

20 The wren, symbol of the RSPB.

22 Detail from the Popey Head at Rattlesden.

23 The Black Dog of Bungay windvane.

24 Civic arms of Newmarket.

25 Lowestoft jug.

26 The Flint Knappers Arms inn at Brandon.

27 Southwold lighthouse.

# ACKNOWLEDGEMENTS

My thanks to my husband, Ray, for his interest and his many helpful suggestions and to Di and Dick Spring of Amber House, Southwold for their hospitality. I would also like to record my thanks to the staff at the Tourist Information Centres in Aldeburgh, Bury St Edmunds, Felixstowe, Ipswich and Woodbridge.

# BIBLIOGRAPHY

*AA Illustrated Guide to Britain.* Sixth edition. Drive Publications 1984.
*A Day Out in Aldeburgh, Snape, Orford* by Terry Palmer. Heritage House.
*A Day Out in Southwold, Walberswick, Dunwich* by Terry Palmer. Heritage House.
*Apple Acre* by Adrian Bell. Bodley Head 1942.
*A Suffolk Calendar* by Allan Jobson. Robert Hale 1966.
*Portrait of Suffolk* by Allan Jobson. Robert Hale 1973.
*Ruth Rendell's Suffolk* by Paul Bowden.
*Suffolk and Norfolk* by M R James. Alastair Press.
*Suffolk Villages* by Allan Jobson. Robert Hale 1971.
*Suffolk* by Arthur Mee. King's England Series. Hodder and Stoughton.
*Suffolk* by Nikolaus Pevsner. Radcliffe.
*The Norfolk-Essex Border* by John Salmon. Boydell Press, Ipswich 1977.
*The Suffolk Landscape* by Norman Scarfe. Hodder and Stoughton 1972.
*Timpson 's England* by John Timpson. Jarrold Publications.
*Suffolk Villages* by Allan Jobson. Robert Hale 1971.
*Portrait of Suffolk* by Allan Jobson. Robert Hale 1973.
*The Suffolk Landscape* by Norman Scarfe. Hodder and Stoughton 1972

**Answers to cover and title page picture questions.**
*Front cover: Thorpeness. This folly, overlooking the sea and golf course, now offers self-catering accommodation.*
*Title page:  It is the Abbey Gate, Bury St Edmunds.*
*Back cover: Hadleigh. The gatehouse is all that is left of the palace built by Archdeacon Pykenham in the fifteenth century.*